Duncles 50 Great

GW00992838

A BUNCH OF THYME	
ALL FOR ME GROG	
AS I ROVED OUT	
BARD OF ARMAGH, THE	34
BEAUTIFUL CITY	31
BLACK VELVET BAND, THE	14
BOLD O'DONOGHUE, THE	23
BOSTON CITY	11
BOTANY BAY	23
BOULAVOGUE	19
BOYS OF FAIR HILL, THE	22
BUTCHER BOY, THE	11
COBBLER, THE	32
CURRAGH OF KILDARE, THE	4
FIELDS OF ATHENRY, THE	22
FOLLOW ME UP TO CARLOW	33
GALWAY RACES, THE	29
GOLDEN JUBILEE, THE	17
GREEN FIELDS OF FRANCE, THE	3
HENRY MY SON	35
I KNOW WHERE I'M GOING	24
I'LL TELL ME MA	20
I'M A ROVER AND SELDOM SOBER	25
IF I WAS A BLACKBIRD	3
JAMES CONNOLLY	26
JOHNNY I HARDLY KNEW YEH	39
JOLLY BEGGAR, THE	30
JUG OF PUNCH	30
KELLY THE BOY FROM KILLANE	0
KERRY RECRUIT, THE	7
LANIGAN'S BALL	37
LARK IN THE CLEAR AIR, THE	25
LOOK AT THE COFFIN	38
MARY HAMILTON	19
MARY MAC	15
MRS. MCGRATH	18
MUIRSHEEN DURKIN	12
MY OWN DEAR GALWAY BAY	33
ON THE BANKS OF THE ROSES	7
PEGGY GORDON	31
RAGLAN ROAD	27
RED IS THE ROSE	15
ROSE OF ALLENDALE, THE	27
SHORES OF AMERIKAY, THE	12
SONG FOR IRELAND	10
STILL I LOVE HIM	8
TOWN OF BALLYBAY, THE	38
TWENTY-ONE YEARS	10
WAXIES DARGLE, THE	6
WEST'S AWAKE, THE	26

Photographs from the Father Francis Brown (1880-1960) collection
have been used with the kind permission of the administrators.
Cover photo by Pat O'Dea: - Traditional Music at the Fleadh Cheoil,
Clonmel, Co. Tipperary. Courtesy of Bord Fáilte.

Layout, Design and Typesetting by Grace O'Halloran.
Cover by Niche Design, Dublin.

Printed by Watermans, Cork.

Ossian Publications Ltd., P.O. Box 84, Cork, Ireland

OMB 81

ISBN 0 946005 62 1

THE GREEN FIELDS OF FRANCE

G   Em   Am   D
Well, how do you do, young Willie McBride,
                   C   G
Do you mind if I sit here down by your graveside,
        Em   Am
And rest for a while 'neath the warm summer sun,
    D   G
I've been working all day and I'm nearly done.
                      Am
I see by your gravestone you were only nineteen,
       D   G   D
When you joined the great fallen in nineteen sixteen,
G   C   Am
I hope you died well and I hope you died clean,
     D   G
Or young Willie McBride was it slow and obscene.

CHORUS:
     D   C   G
Did they beat the drum slowly, did they play the fife lowly.
     D   C   D
Did they sound the dead march as they lowered you down,
    C   G
And did the band play the Last Post and chorus,
    Em   D G
Did the pipes play the Flow'rs of the Forest.

And did you leave a wife or a sweetheart behind,
In some faithful heart is your memory enshrined.
Although you died back in nineteen sixteen,
In that faithful heart are you forever nineteen.
Or are you a stranger without even a name,
Enclosed and forever behind the glass frame,
In an old photograph, torn and battered and stained
And faded to yellow in a brown leather frame.
REPEAT CHORUS

The sun now it shines on the green fields of France
There's a warm summer breeze, it makes the red poppies dance.
And look how the sun shines from under the clouds
There's no gas, no barbed wire, no guns firing now.
But here in this graveyard it's still no-man's-land.
The countless white crosses stand mute in the sand,
To man's blind indifference to his fellow man,
To a whole generation that were butchered and damned.
REPEAT CHORUS

Now young Willie McBride I can't help but wonder why
Do all those who lie here know why they died.
And did they believe when they answered the cause
Did they really believe that this war would end wars.
Well the sorrows, the suffering, the glory, the pain
The killing and dying was all done in vain.
For young Willie McBride it all happened again,
And again, and again, and again, and again.
REPEAT CHORUS

IF I WAS A BLACKBIRD

G
I am a young maiden
             D
And my story is sad,

For once I was courted
       G   D
By a brave sailor lad.
   G
He courted me strongly
            D
By night and by day,

But now my dear sailor
           G
Is gone far away.

CHORUS:
G
If I was a blackbird
            D
I'd whistle and sing,

And I'd follow the ship
         G   D
That my true love sails in,
G
And on the top riggings
            D
I'd there build my nest,

And I'd pillow my head
            G
On his lily white breast.

He promised to take me
To Donnybrook fair
To buy me red ribbon
To bind up my hair.
And when he'd return
From the ocean so wide,
He'd take me and make me
His own loving bride.
REPEAT CHORUS

His parents they slight me
And will not agree
That I and my sailor
Married should be.
But when he comes home
I will greet him with joy
And I'll take to my bosom
My dear sailor boy.
REPEAT CHORUS

A BUNCH OF THYME

D   A   D
Come all you maidens young and fair,

                          A
All you that are blooming in your prime

    D
And always beware, to keep your

Em   D A
garden fair,

    D   A   D
Let no man steal away your thyme

              A   D
For thyme it is a precious thing,

                       A
And thyme brings all things to my mind
D   G
Thyme with all its flavours, along with

Em   D A
all its joys,

D   A   D
Thyme brings all things to my mind.

Once I had a bunch of thyme,
I thought it never would decay
Then came a lusty sailor, who chanced to
pass my way,
And stole my bunch of thyme away.

Come all ye, etc.

The sailor gave to me a rose,
A rose that never would decay
He gave it to me to keep me reminded
Of when he stole my thyme away.

Come all ye, etc.

THE CURRAGH OF KILDARE

G
The winter it is past
C   D
And the summer's come at last

And the small birds they sing on every tree;
                                 G
Their little hearts are glad,
            C   D
But mine is very sad,
         G   C   D
Since my true love is far away from me.

The rose upon the briar,
By the water running clear,
Gives joy to the linnet and the bee;
Their little hearts are blest,
But mine is not at rest,
While my true love is absent from me.

A livery I'll wear,
And I'll comb back my hair,
And in velvet so green I will appear;
And straight I will repair
To the Curragh of Kildare,
For it's there I'll find tidings of my dear.

I'll wear a cap of black,
With a frill around my neck,
Gold rings on my fingers I wear;
It's this I undertake,
For my true lover's sake,
He resides at the Curragh of Kildare.

I would not think it strange,
Thus the world for to range,
If I only got tidings of my dear;
But here in Cupid's chain,
If I'm bound to remain,
I would spend my whole life in despair.

My love is like the sun,
That in the firmament does run;
And always proves constant and true;
But his is like the moon,
That wanders up and down,
And every month is new.

All you that are in love
And cannot it remove,
I pity the pains you endure;
For experience let me know,
That your hearts are full of woe,
And a woe that no mortal can cure.

Apple picking at Good Shepherd Convent, Limerick, 1938

KELLY THE BOY FROM KILLANE

D
What's the news, what's the news,
G
Oh, my bold Shelmalier,
D   A   D
With your long barrel'd gun of the sea,

Say, what wind from the south
G
Blows his messenger here,
D   A   D
With a hymn of the dawn for the free.
G
Goodly news, goodly news,
D
Do I bring youth of Forth,
G   A
Goodly news you shall hear, Bargey men,
D
For the boys march at dawn
G
From the south to the north,
D   A   D
Led by Kelly, the boy from Killane.

Tell me who is the giant
With the gold curling hair,
He who rides at the head of your band;
Seven feet is his height,
With some inches to spare,
And he looks like a king in command.
'Oh me boys, that's the pride
Of the bold Shelmaliers,
'Mongst our greatest of heroes, a Man.'
Fling your beavers aloft
And give three rousing cheers,
For John Kelly, the boy from Killane.

Enniscorthy's in flames
And old Wexford is won,
And the Barrow tomorrow we cross,
On a hill o'er the town
We have planted a gun,
That will batter the gateways to Ross.
All the Forth men and Bargey men
March o'er the heath,
With brave Harvey to lead on the van;
But the foremost of all
In that grim gap of death,
Will be Kelly, the boy from Killane.

But the gold sun of freedom
Grew darkened at Ross
And it set by the Slaney's red waves,
And poor Wexford stripped naked,
Hung high on a cross,
With her heart pierced by traitors and slaves.
Glory O, Glory O
To her brave sons who died,
For the cause of the long-downtrodden man,
Glory O to Mount Leinster's
Own darling and pride,
Dauntless Kelly, the boy of Killane.

THE WAXIES DARGLE

D   G
Says my aul' wan to your aul' wan:
D
'Will yeh come to the Waxies dargle?'
G
Says your aul' wan to my aul' wan:
A   D
'Sure I haven't got a farthing,

I've just been down to Monto town
G   A
To see uncle McArdle,
D   G
But he wouldn't lend me half a crown
A   D
For to go to the Waxies dargle.'

Says my aul' wan to your aul' wan:
'Will you come to the Galway Races?'
Says your aul' wan to my aul' wan:
'With the price of my aul' lad's braces
I went down to Capel Street
To the Jew man moneylenders.
But they wouldn't give me a couple of bob on
My aul' lad's suspenders.'

Says my aul' wan to your aul' wan:
'We have no beef or mutton.
But if we go down to Monto town,
We might get a drink for nuttin'.
Here's a piece of advice
I from an aul' fishmonger
When food is scarce and you see the hearse
You'll know you have died of hunger.'

THE KERRY RECRUIT

D   A
About four years ago, I was digging the land,

                      D
With my brogues on my feet and my spade in my hand.

             A
Says I to myself what a pity to see,

                  D
Such a fine strapping lad footing turf in Tralee.

CHORUS:
D   A
Wid me toora na nya, and me toora na nya,

               D
Wid me toora na noora na noora na nya.

So I buttoned my brogues and shook hands with my spade,
And I went to the fair like a dashing young blade,
When up comes the sergeant and asks me to 'list,
'Arra, Sergeant, a gra, put the bob in my fist.'
REPEAT CHORUS

And the first thing they gave me it was a red coat,
With a wide strap of leather to tie round my throat,
They gave me a quare thing, I asked what was that,
And they told me it was a cockade for my hat.
REPEAT CHORUS

The next thing they gave me, they called it a gun,
With powder and shot and a place for my thumb;
And first she spit fire and then she spit smoke,
Lord, she gave a great lep and my shoulder near broke.
REPEAT CHORUS

The next place they sent me was down to the sea,
On board of a warship bound for the Crimea,
Three sticks in the middle all rowled round with sheets,
Faith, she walked thro' the water without any feet.
REPEAT CHORUS

We fought at the Alma, likewise Inkermann,
But the Russians they whaled us at the Redan,
In scaling the walls there myself lost my eye,
And a big Russian bullet ran off with my thigh.
REPEAT CHORUS

It was there I lay bleeding, stretched on the cold ground,
Heads, legs and arms were scattered all around,
Says I, if my man or my cleaveens were nigh,
They'd bury me decent and raise a loud cry.
REPEAT CHORUS

They brought me the doctor, who soon staunched my blood,
And he gave me an elegant leg made of wood,
They gave me a medal and tenpence a day,
Contented with Sheela, I'll live on half-pay.
REPEAT CHORUS

ON THE BANKS OF THE ROSES

D
On the banks of the Roses,

     A   D
My love and I sat down

          G   D
And I took out my fiddle

     A   D
To play my love a tune,

In the middle of the tune, oh,

        A   D
She sighed and she said:

                  G
'O-ro Johnny, lovely Johnny,

         A   D
Would you leave me.'

Oh when I was a young man
I heard my father say,
That he'd rather see me dead
And buried in the clay,
Sooner than be married
To any runaway,
By the lovely sweet
Banks of the Roses.

Oh then I am no runaway
And soon I'll let them know,
I can take a good glass
Or can leave it alone;
And the man that doesn't like me,
He can keep his daughter at home,
And young Johnny will
Go roving with another.

And if ever I get married
'Twill be in the month of May,
When the leaves they are green
And the meadows they are gay,
And I and my true love can sit
And sport and play,
On the lovely sweet
Banks of the Roses.

STILL I LOVE HIM

```
D                    A          D
When I was single I wore a black shawl,
                          A
Now that I'm married I've nothing at all.
```

CHORUS:
```
G    D        G    D
Still I love him, I'll forgive him,
G    D            A      D
I'll go with him wherever he goes.
```

He stands at the corner and whistles me out,
His hands in his pockets, his shirt hanging out.
REPEAT CHORUS

He bought me handkerchief red white and blue,
And then to clean windows he tore it in two.
REPEAT CHORUS

He comes down our alley and whistles me out,
And when I get out there he knocks me about.
REPEAT CHORUS

He took me to the alehouse and bought me some stout,
Before I could drink it he ordered me out.
REPEAT CHORUS

Glendalough, Co. Wicklow, 1933

SONG FOR IRELAND

G   D
Walking all the day
    C   G
Near tall towers where falcons build their nests.
              D
Silver winged they fly
    C   G
They know the call of freedom in their breasts.
C   G
Saw Black Head against the sky
                        D
Where twisted rocks they run to the sea.

CHORUS:
C   G
Living on your western shore
                    D
Saw summer sunsets asked for more
 C   G   D
I stood by your Atlantic Sea
     C   G
And sang a song for Ireland.

Talking all the day,
With true friends who try to make you stay
Telling jokes and news,
Singing songs to pass the night away.
Watched the Galway salmon run,
Like silver, dancing, darting in the sun.
REPEAT CHORUS

Drinking all the day,
In old pubs where fiddlers love to play,
Saw one touch the bow,
He played a reel which seemed so grand and gay.
Stood on Dingle beach and cast,
In wild foam we found Atlantic bass.
REPEAT CHORUS

Dreaming in the night,
I saw a land where no-one has to fight
Waking in your dawn,
I saw you crying in the morning light,
Lying where the falcons fly,
They twist and turn all in your air blue sky.
REPEAT CHORUS

TWENTY-ONE YEARS

D
The judge said 'Stand up, lad,
                      A
And dry up your tears.

You're sentenced to Dartmoor
                D
For twenty-one years.'

So dry up your tears, love,
                A
And kiss me goodbye,

The best friends must part, love,
                D
So must you and I.

I hear the train coming,
'Twill be here at nine.
To take me to Dartmoor
To serve up my time.
I look down the railway
And plainly I see,
You standing there waving
Your goodbyes to me.

Six months have gone by, love,
I wish I were dead.
This dark dreary dungeon
And stone for my bed.
It's hailing, it's raining,
The moon gives no light.
Now won't you tell me, love,
Why you never write?

I've counted the days, love,
I've counted the nights,
I've counted the footsteps,
I've counted the lights,
I've counted the raindrops,
I've counted the stars,
I've counted a million
Of these prison bars.

I've waited, I've trusted,
I've longed for the day,
A lifetime, so lonely,
Now my hair's turning grey.
My thoughts are for you, love,
Till I'm out of my mind,
For twenty-one years
Is a mighty long time.

BOSTON CITY

D   G   D A
I was born in Boston city boys,
  D
A place you all know well
      G   A   D
Brought up by honest parents,
          A
The truth to you I'll tell,
      D   G   D A
Brought up by honest parents,
    D
And raised most tenderly,
   G   A   D
Till I became a sporting blade
       A   D
At the age of twenty three.

My character it was taken
And I was sent to jail,
My parents thought to bail me out,
But they found it all in vain;
The jury found me guilty,
And the clerk he wrote it down,
The judge he passed my sentence
And I was sent to Charlestown.

I see my aged father
And he standing by the Bar,
Likewise my aged mother
And she tearing off her hair;
The tearing of her old grey locks
And the tears came mingled down,
Saying, 'John, my son, what have you done,
That you're bound for Charlestown.'

There's a girl in Boston city boys,
A place you all know well
And if e'er I get my liberty,
It's with her I will dwell.
If e'er I get my liberty,
Bad company I will shun,
The robbing of the Munster bank,
And the drinking of rum.

You lads that are at liberty,
Should keep it while you can,
Don't roam the street by night or day,
Or break the laws of man,
For if you do you're sure to rue
And become a lad like me,
A-serving up your twenty-one years,
In the Royal Artillery.

THE BUTCHER BOY

D   A   D
In London town, where I did dwell,
         Em   D
A butcher boy I loved him well,
                 A
He courted me, for many a day,
                 D
He stole from me, my heart away.

CHORUS:
I wish, I wish, I wish in vain,
I wish I was a maid again,
A maid again I ne'er can be,
Till apples grow on an ivy tree.

There is an inn in that same town
And there my love he sits him down;
He takes a strange girl on his knee
And tells her what he wouldn't tell me.
REPEAT CHORUS

The reason is I'll tell you why,
Because she's got more gold than I,
But gold will melt and silver fly
And in time of need be as poor as I.
REPEAT CHORUS

I'll go upstairs and make my bed,
'There's nothing to do,' my mother said.
My mother she has followed me,
Saying 'what is the matter, my daughter dear.'
REPEAT CHORUS

'Oh mother dear, you little know
What pains and sorrows or what woe.
Go get a chair and sit me down
With pen and ink I'll write all down.'
REPEAT CHORUS

Her father he came home that night,
Enquiring for his heart's delight,
He went upstairs, the door he broke,
He found her hanging on a rope.
REPEAT CHORUS

He took a knife and cut her down
And in her bosom these lines he found:
'Oh what a foolish girl was I
To hang myself for a butcher's boy.'
REPEAT CHORUS

'Go dig my grave both wide and deep,
Put a marble stone at my head and feet,
And on my grave place a turtle dove,
To show the world that I died for love.'
REPEAT CHORUS

THE SHORES OF AMERIKAY

```
G                        C
I'm bidding farewell to the land of
 G
my youth
     D              G
And the home I love so well,
        D                       C
And the mountains so grand in my own

native land,
 G                       D
I am bidding them all farewell.
                    C
With an achin' heart I'll bid them adieu,
 G                  D
For tomorrow I'll sail far away,
        G          C      G
O'er the raging foam to seek a home
    D               G
On the shores of Amerikay.
```

It's not for the want of employment I'm
going,
It's not for the love of fame,
That fortune bright may shine over me,
And give me a glorious name.
It's not for the want of employment I'm
going,
O'er the weary and stormy sea,
But to seek a home for my own true
love,
On the shores of Amerikay.

And when I'm bidding my last farewell,
The tears like rain will blind,
To think of my friends in my own
native land
And the home I'm leaving behind.
But if I'm to die in a foreign land,
And be buried so far away,
No fond mother's tears will be shed
o'er my grave
On the shores of Amerikay.

MUIRSHEEN DURKIN

```
C                       G
In the days I went a-courtin'
                           C
I was never tired resorting
                              G
To the ale-house and the play-house
                        C
And many a house beside,
                          G
But I told my brother Seamus
                           C
I'll be off now and grow famous,
                           G
And before I come home again
                        C
I'll roam the world wide.
```

Oh, I courted girls in Blarney,
In Kanturk and in Killarney,
In Passage and in Queenstown,
I mean the Cobh of Cork.
But I'm tired of all this pleasure,
So now I'll take my leisure
And the next time that you hear
from me
Be a letter from New York.

So goodbye Muirsheen Durkin,
Sure I'm sick and tired of workin'
No more I'll dig the praties,
No longer I'll be fooled:
But as sure as my name is Carney,
I'll be off to Californee,
And instead of diggin' praties,
I'll be diggin' lumps of gold.

Goodbye to all the boys at home,
I'm sailing far across the foam,
To try and make my fortune
In far Amerikay.
For there's gold and money plenty,
For the poor and for the gentry,
And when I'm back again,
I never more will stray.

Emigrating from the White Star Line Wharf, Cobh, Co. Cork, 1912

13

THE BLACK VELVET BAND

D   A
As I went walking down broadway, not intending to stay very long,
D   A   D
I met with a frolicsome damsel as she came tripping along.
D   ·
A watch she pulled out of her pocket, and slipped it right into my hand
        D   A   D
On the very first day that I met her, bad luck to the black velvet band.

CHORUS:
D   A
Her eyes they shone like diamonds, you'd think she was queen of the land,
D   A   D
With her hair thrown over her shoulder, tied up with a black velvet band.

'Twas in the town of Tralee
An apprentice to trade I was bound,
With a-plenty of bright amusement
To see the days go round.
Till misfortune and trouble came over me,
Which caused me to stray from my land,
Far away from my friends and relations,
To follow the Black Velvet Band.

Before the judge and the jury
The both of us had to appear,
And a gentleman swore to the jewellery -
The case against us was clear,
For seven years transportation
Right unto Van Dieman's Land,
Far away from my friends and relations,
To follow her Black Velvet Band.

Oh all you brave young Irish lads,
A warning take by me,
Beware of the pretty young damsels
That are knocking around in Tralee.
They'll treat you to whiskey and porter,
Until you're unable to stand,
And before you have time for to leave them,
You are unto Van Dieman's Land.

MARY MAC

Em
There's a little girl and her name is Mary Mac
D
Make no mistake she's the girl I'm goin' to track,
Em   D
Lots of other fellows they get upon her track,
        Em
But I'm thinkin' that they'd have to get up early.

CHORUS:
Mary Mac's father's making Mary Mac marry me,
My father's making me marry Mary Mac.
Gonna marry Mary for my Mary to take care of me,
We'll be feeling merry when I marry Mary Mac

Well this little lass she has a lot of class,
Got a lot of brass and her father thinks I'm gas.
And I'd be a silly ass for to let the matter pass,
My father says she suits me really fairly.
REPEAT CHORUS

Mary and her mother go an awful lot together,
In fact you'd hardly see the one without the other,
And the people wonder whether it is Mary or her Mother,
Or the both of them together that I'm courting.
REPEAT CHORUS

The Wedding's on a Wednesday and everything's
arranged,
Soon her name will change to mine unless her mind is
changed.
And with making the arrangements I'm just about
deranged,
Marriage is an awful undertaking.
REPEAT CHORUS

Sure to be a grand affair and grander than a fair,
There's going to be a coach and pair for every pair that's
there,
We'll dine upon the finest fair I'm sure to get me share,
If I don't I'll be very much mistaken.
REPEAT CHORUS

RED IS THE ROSE

D   A
Come over the hills, my bonnie
                  G
Irish lass,
D
Come over the hills to your
G   A
darling.
G   D
You choose the rose love, and
G
I'll make the vow,
      D   G   D
And I'll be your true love
        A D
forever.

CHORUS:
Red is the rose that in yonder
garden grows,
And fair is the lily of the valley.
Clear is the water that flows
from the Boyne,
But my love is fairer than any.

'Twas down by Killarney's
green woods that we strayed,
And the moon and the stars
they were shining,
The moon shone its rays on
her locks of golden hair,
And she swore she'd be my
love forever.
REPEAT CHORUS

It's not for the parting that my
sister pains,
It's not for the grief of my
mother,
'Tis all for the loss of my
bonnie Irish lass,
That my heart is breaking
forever.
REPEAT CHORUS

15

Loading up, Tralee, Co. Kerry, 1932

THE GOLDEN JUBILEE

G   C
Way down in the County Kerry, in the place they call Tralee,
G   D
A fine old couple they lived there, called Kate and Pat McGee;
       G   C
They were goin' to hold a party on their Golden Jubilee,
    G   C   G
And Kate said she to Pat McGee 'Come listen here to me.'

CHORUS:
G   C
'Put on your oul' knee breeches, and your coat of em'rald green,
G   Am   D
Take off that hat, me darlin' Pat, put on your oul' Caubeen,
     G   C
For today's our Golden Wedding, and we want them all to know,
G   C   G
The way we looked when we were wed, just fifty years ago.'

Ah, well do I remember when we danced on the village green,
You held me in your arms, dear Pat, and called me your colleen.
Your hair was like the raven's wing, but now 'tis turning grey,
Come over here, oul' sweetheart dear, and hear what I've to say.
REPEAT CHORUS

Ah, well do I remember when first I was your bride,
In the little chapel yonder there, where we sat side by side.
Of good things we've had many, of troubles we've had few:
Come over here, oul' sweetheart dear, and here's what you must do.
REPEAT CHORUS

17

MRS. MCGRATH

D   A
'Oh, missus McGrath,' the sergeant said,
      D   A
'Would you like to make a soldier out of your son Ted,
      D   G   D   A
With a scarlet coat and a big cocked hat,
     D   A   D
Now missus McGrath, wouldn't you like that?

CHORUS:

D   G   D
Wid yer too ri aa, fol the diddle aa,
          A   D
Too ri, too ri, too ri, aa.
      G   D
Wid yer too ri aa, fol the diddle aa,
         A   D
Too ri, too ri, too ri, aa.

So Mrs. McGrath lived on the sea-shore,
For the space of seven long years or more,
Till she saw a big ship sailing into the bay,
'Here's my son Ted, wisha, clear the way.'
REPEAT CHORUS

'Oh captain dear, where have you been,
Have you been sailing the Mediterreen,
Or have you any tidings of my son Ted,
Is the poor boy living, or is he dead?'
REPEAT CHORUS

Then up comes Ted without any legs,
And in their place he has two wooden pegs.
She kissed him a dozen times or two,
Saying 'Holy Moses, 'tisn't you.'
REPEAT CHORUS

'Oh then were you drunk or were you blind,
That yeh left yer two fine legs behind,
Or was it walking upon the sea,
Wore yer two fine legs from the knees away?'
REPEAT CHORUS

'Oh no I wasn't drunk or blind,
When I left my two fine legs behind,
For a cannonball on the fifth of May,
Took my two fine legs from the knees away.'
REPEAT CHORUS

'Oh then Teddy me boy,' the widow cried,
'Yer two fine legs were yer mammy's pride
Them stumps of a tree wouldn't do at all,
Why didn't you run from the big
cannonball?'
REPEAT CHORUS

'All foreign wars I do proclaim
Between Don John and the King of Spain,
And by herrins I'll make them rue the time
That they swept the legs of a child of mine.'
REPEAT CHORUS

'Oh then if I had you back again,
I'd never let you go to fight the King of Spain,
For I'd rather have my Ted as he used to be,
Than the King of France and his whole Navy.'
REPEAT CHORUS

ALL FOR ME GROG

G
And it's all for me grog,
      C   G
Me jolly, jolly grog,
                      D
All for me beer and tobacco
        G
For I spent all me tin
          C   G
On the lassies drinking gin
                      D
Far across the Western Ocean
        G
I must wander.

Where are me boots,
Me noggin', noggin' boots,
They're all gone for beer and tobacco.
For the heels they are worn out
And the toes are kicked about,
And the soles are looking out
For better weather.

Where is me shirt,
Me noggin', noggin' shirt,
It's all gone for beer and tobacco,
For the collar is all worn,
And the sleeves they are all torn,
And the tail is looking out
For better weather.

I'm sick in the head
And I haven't been to bed,
Since I first came onhore.
From me slumber,
For I spent all me dough
On the lassies don't you know,
Far across the Western Ocean
I must wander.

BOULAVOGUE

```
D              G            D              Em      A
At Boulavogue as the sun was setting o'er bright May meadows of Shelmalier,
D              G            D                  A        D
A rebel hand set the heather blazing, and brought the neighbours from far and near.
                  G                D                Em
Then Father Murphy from old Kilcormack spurred up the rocks with a warning cry:
A    D                  G            D            A        D
'Arm, arm', he cried, 'For I've come to lead you,for Ireland's freedom we fight or die.'
```

He led us 'gainst coming soldiers, and the cowardly Yeomen were put to flight;
'Twas at the Barrow, the boys of Wexford, showed Bookey's regiment how men could fight.
Look out for hirelings, King George of England, search every kingdom where breathes a slave,
For Father Murphy from the County Wexford sweeps o'er the land like a mighty wave.

We took Camolin and Enniscorthy, and Wexford, storming, drove out our foes;
'Twas at Slieve Coillte our pikes were reeking with the crimson stream of the beaten Yeo's.
At Tubberneering and Ballyellis full many a Hessian lay in his gore;
Ah, Father Murphy, had aid come over, the green flag floated from shore to shore.

At Vinegar Hill, o'er the pleasant Slaney, our heroes vainly stood back to back.
And the Yeo's at Tullow took Father Murphy, and burned his body upon the rack.
God grant you glory, brave Father Murphy, and open heaven to all your men;
The cause that called you may call tomorrow, in another fight for the green again.

MARY HAMILTON

```
D                  G  D                    A
Last night there were four Marys, this night there'll be but three;
            G  A      D              A        D
There were Mary Beaton and Mary Seaton and Mary Carmichael and me.
```

Oh, how often have I dressed my queen and put gold upon her hair,
But now I've gotten for my reward the gallows to be my share.

Last night I dressed queen Mary and put on her braw silk gown,
And all the thanks I've got this night is to be hanged in Edinboro town.

They'll tie a kerchief round my eyes, they'll no let me see to dee,
And they'll never tell my father and mother but that I'm away o'er the sea.

I charge all ye sailors, when ye sail o'er the foam,
Let neither my father nor mother know but that I'm coming home.

Oh, little did my mother think, the day she cradled me,
The lands I was to travel in or the death I was to dee.

Last night there were four Marys, this night there'll be but three;
There were Mary Beaton and Mary Seaton and Mary Carmichael and me.

braw - handsome, well-dressed.
dee - die.

19

I'LL TELL ME MA

G
I'll tell me ma, when I go home,
    D   G
The boys won't leave the girls

alone.

They pull my hair, they stole

my comb
        D   G
And that's all right till I go

home.

                C
She is handsome, she is pretty,
G   D
She is the belle of Belfast city,
G   C
She is courtin', one two three,
G   D   G
Please won't you tell me who

is she?

Albert Mooney says he loves
her,
All the boys are fighting for her,
They rap at the door and
they ring at the bell,
Saying 'Oh my true-love are
you well?'
Out she comes as white as snow
Rings on her fingers,
bells on her toes,
Old Jenny Murphy says
she'll die,
If she doesn't get the fellow
with the roving eye.

Let the wind and the rain
and the hail blow high
And the snow come
shovelling from the sky
She's as nice as apple pie
And she'll get her own lad
by and by.
When she gets a lad of her own
She won't tell her ma when
she gets home
Let them all come as they will,
But its Albert Mooney
she loves still.

Swinging on the pump, Leighlin Bridge, Co. Carlow, 1

THE BOYS OF FAIR HILL

G
Come boys, spend a day
        Am   D
With our Harrier Club so gay:
G
The cry of the hounds
            D
It will make your heart thrill.
G
And when you hear Connie Doyle say:
        Am   D
'The Armoured Car has won today'
G   D   G   D   G
Here's up 'em all say the boys of Fair Hill.

First you go to Fahy's well
For a drink of pure, clear water,
The finest spot on earth
Sure the angels do say,
Where thousands come across the foam,
Just to view the Blarney Stone,

Which can be seen from the groves of Fair
Hill.

First you go to Quinlan's pub -
That is where you join our club,
Where round us in gallons
The porter does flow;
First they tap half-a-tierce
And drink a health to Dashwood's race:

That's the stuff to give 'em say the boys of
Fair hill.

Come boys and spend a day
With our hurling club so gay;
The clash of the ash
It will make your heart thrill.
The Rockies thought that they were stars,
Till they met the Saint Finbarr's,

Here's up 'em all say the boys of Fair Hill.

THE FIELDS OF ATHENRY

G
By the lonely prison wall
  C   G   D
I heard a young girl calling,
G   C   D
Michael, they are taking you away,
         G   C
For you stole Trevelyn's corn,
       G   D
So the young might see the morn,
                          G
Now a prison ship lies waiting in the bay.

CHORUS:
G   C   G
Low, lie the fields of Athenry,
                                D
Where once we watched the small free birds fly
G   C
Our love was on the wing,
     G   D
We had dreams and songs to sing
                                G
It's so lonely 'round the fields of Athenry.

By a lonely prison wall
I heard a young man calling,
Nothing matters Mary when you're free,
Against the Famine and the Crown,
I rebelled they ran me down,
Now you must raise our child with dignity.
REPEAT CHORUS

By a lonely harbour wall
She watched the last star falling
And that prison ship sailed out against the
sky.
Sure she'll wait and hope and pray
For her love in Botany Bay,
It's so lonely round the fields of Athenry.
REPEAT CHORUS

BOTANY BAY

CHORUS:

G
Farewell to your bricks and mortar,
C   G
Farewell to your dirty lies,

Farewell with your gangers and gang planks,
 D
To hell with your overtime.
    G
For the good ship Ragamuffin
    C   G   D
She's lying at the Quay,
    Em
To take oul Pat with a shovel on his back

To the shores of Botany Bay.

I'm on my way down to the Quay
Where the ship at anchor lays,
To command a gang of navvys
That they told me to engage,
I thought I'd drop in for a drink
Before I went away,
For to take a trip on an emigrant ship
To the shores of Botany Bay.
REPEAT CHORUS

The boss came up this morning,
He says, 'well Pat you know,
If you don't get your navvys out
I'm afraid you'll have to go.'
So I asked him for my wages
And demanded all my pay,
For I told him straight I'm going to emigrate
To the shores of Botany Bay.
REPEAT CHORUS

And when I reach Australia,
I'll go and look for gold,
There's plenty there for the digging of
Or so I have been told.
Or else I'll go back to my trade
And a hundred bricks I'll lay,
Because I live for an eight hour shift
On the shores of Botany Bay.
REPEAT CHORUS

THE BOLD O'DONOGHUE

G
Here I am from Paddy's land,
    C
A land of high renown,
    D
I broke the hearts of all the girls
         G
From miles of Keady town,

And when they hear that I'm awa'
    C
They raise a hullabaloo,
    D
When they hear about the handsome lad
         G
They call O'Donoghue.

CHORUS:
For I'm the boy to please her
And I'm the boy to tease her,
And I'm the boy to squeeze her up
And I'll tell you what I'll do,
I'll court her like an Irishman
With me brogue and blarney too is me plan,
With me rollikin', swollikin', gollikin', wollikin'
Bold O'Donoghue.

I wish me love was a red, red rose
Grown' on yon garden wall,
And me to be a dewdrop
And upon her brow I'd fall,
Perhaps now she might think of me
As a rather heavy dew,
No more she'd love the handsome lad
They call O'Donoghue.
REPEAT CHORUS

They say that Queen Victoria
Has a daughter fine and grand,
Perhaps she'd take it into her head
For to marry an Irishman.
And if I could only get the chance
To have a word or two,
Perhaps she'd take a notion
In the bold O'Donoghue.
REPEAT CHORUS

23

I KNOW WHERE I'M GOING

G   D
I know where I'm going and I know who's going with me,
G   Am   D
I know who I love, but the dear knows who I'll marry.

I'll have stockings of silk, shoes of fine green leather,
Combs to buckle my hair and a ring on every finger.

Feather beds are soft painted rooms are bonny;
But I'd leave them all to go with my love Johnny.

Some say he's dark I say he's bonny,
He's the flower of them all, my handsome, coaxing Johnny.

I know where I'm going I know who's going with me,
I know who I love, but the dear knows who I'll marry.

Jaunting cart, Co. Tipperary, 1929

I'M A ROVER
AND SELDOM SOBER

<pre>
G   C   G
I'm a rover and seldom sober,
                      D
I'm a rover of high degree,
              G
It's when I'm drinking I'm always thinking,
                  D   G
How to gain my love's company.
</pre>

Though the night be as dark as dungeon,
Not a star to be seen above,
I will be guided without a stumble,
Into the arms of my own true love.

He stepped up to her bedroom window,
Kneeling gently upon a stone,
He rapped at her bedroom window,
'Darling dear, do you lie alone?'

It's only me your own true lover,
Open the door and let me in,
For I have come on a long journey
And I'm near drenched to the skin.

She opened the door with the greatest pleasure,
She opened the door and she let him in
They both shook hands and embraced each other,
Until the morning they lay as one.

Now my love, I must go and leave thee
And though the hills they are high above,
I will climb them with greater pleasure,
Since I've been in the arms of my love.

THE LARK IN THE CLEAR AIR

<pre>
G   C   G   D
Dear thoughts are in my mind and my soul soars enchanted
     G   C   G   C D   G
As I hear the sweet lark sing in the clear air of the day.
                                              D
For a tender beaming smile to my hope has been granted,
     G   D   G   C   D   G
And tomorrow she shall hear all my fond heart would say.
</pre>

I shall tell her all my love, all my soul's adoration,
And I think she will hear me and will not say me nay,
It is this that gives my soul all its joyous elation,
As I hear the sweet lark sing in the clear air of the day.

THE WEST'S AWAKE

```
G                    C
When all beside a vigil keep,
    D              G
The west's asleep, the west's asleep.
                  C
Alas, and well may Erin weep,
    D                    G
That Connaught lies in slumber deep.
                        Am
There lake and plain smile fair and free,
            D
'Mid rocks their guardian chivalry,
    G    C            G
Sing: Oh let man learn liberty,
            D              G
From crashing wind and lashing sea.
```

That chainless wave and lovely land,
Freedom and Nationhood demand.
Be sure the great God never planned
For slumb'ring slaves a home so grand.
And long a proud and haughty race
Honour'd and sentinell'd the place.
Sing: Oh not e'en their sons' disgrace
Can quite destroy their glory's trace.

For often in O'Connor's van,
To triumph dashed each Connaught clan
And fleet as deer the Normans ran
Through Curlew's Pass and Ardrahan;
And later times saw deeds as brave,
And glory guards Clanricarde's grave;
Sing: Oh they died their land to save
At Aughrim's slopes and Shannon's wave.

And if, when all a vigil keep,
The west's asleep, the west's asleep
Alas and well may Erin weep
That Connaught lies in slumber deep.
But hark, a voice like thunder spake,
The west's awake, the west's awake.
Sing: Oh hurrah, let England quake
We'll watch till death for Erin's sake.

JAMES CONNOLLY

```
Em                      D      Em
Where oh where is our James Connolly,
                        D      Em
Where oh where is that gallant man?
                  D        G    D
He's gone to organise the union,
Em              D              Em
That working men might yet be free.
```

Where oh where is the Citizen Army,
Where oh where are those fighting men?
They've gone to join the Great Rebellion
And break the bonds of slavery.

And who'll be there to lead the van
O, who'll be there to lead the van?
Who should be there but our James
Connolly
The hero of each working man.

Who carries high that burning flag,
Who carries high that burning flag?
'Tis our James Connolly all pale and
wounded,
Who carries high our burning flag.

They carried him up to the jail,
They carried him up to the jail.
There they shot him one bright May
morning
And quickly laid him in his grave.

Who mourns now for our James Connolly,
Who mourns for the fighting man?
O lay me down in yon green garden,
And make my bearers Union men.

We laid him down in yon green garden,
With Union men on every side,
And swore we'd make one mighty Union,
And fill that gallant man with pride.

Now all you noble Irishmen
Come join with me for liberty,
And we will forge a mighty weapon,
And smash the bonds of slavery!

THE ROSE OF ALLENDALE

```
G                    C         G                        D
The morn was fair, the skies were clear, no breath came o'er the sea,
     G        C        G              D      G
When Mary left her highland home and wandered forth with me.
          C          G                          D
Though flowers deck'd the mountainside and fragrance fill'd the vale,
G            C        G            D    G
By far the sweetest flower there was the rose of Allendale.
```

CHORUS:
```
G              C      Am            D
Was the rose of Allendale, was the rose of Allendale,
G            C        G            D    G
By far the sweetest flower there was the rose of Allendale.
```

```
Where'er I wandered, east or west, tho' fate began to lour,
A solace still she was to me,in sorrow's lonely hour.
When tempests lashed our lonely barque, and rent her shiv'ring sail,
One maiden form withstood the storm, - 'twas the Rose of Allendale.
REPEAT CHORUS
```

```
And when my fever'd lips were parched on Afric's burning sands,
She whispered hopes of happiness and tales of distant lands.
My life has been a wilderness unblest by fortune's gale;
Had fate not linked my lot to hers, the Rose of Allendale.
REPEAT CHORUS
```

RAGLAN ROAD

```
D                         G    D
On Raglan Road of an Autumn day, I saw her first and knew
G                  D                        A
That her dark hair would weave a snare that I might one day rue.
G          D                    A
I saw the danger and I passed, along the enchanted way,
     D              G      D
And I said let grief be a fallen leaf at the dawning of the day.
```

```
On Grafton Street in November we tripped lightly along the ledge
Of a deep ravine where can be seen the worth of passion play,
The Queen of Hearts still making tarts and I not making hay,
Oh, I loved too much and by such and such
Is happiness thrown away.
```

```
I gave her gifts of the mind, I gave her secret signs
That's known to the artists who have known the true gods of sound and stone,
And her words and tint without stint, I gave her poems to say,
With her own name there and her own dark hair
Like clouds over fields of May.
```

```
On a quiet street where old ghosts meet, I see her walking now,
Away from me so hurriedly, my reason must allow,
That I had loved not as I should, a creature made of clay,
When the angel woos the clay he'll lose
His wings at the dawn of day.
```

Spanish Arch, Galway City, 1939

THE GALWAY RACES

```
C
As I roved out to Galway town to seek for recreation,
        Am              G              C
On the seventeenth of August my mind was elevated,
                   G              Am          C
There were multitudes assembled with their tickets at the station,
                                            Am
My eyes began to dazzle and they goin' to see the races.
```

CHORUS:
```
          C         G         Am
With me whack fol the do, fol the diddeley idle ay.
```

There were passengers from Limerick and passengers from Nenagh
And passengers from Dublin and sportsmen from Tipp'rary.
There were passengers from Kerry and all the quarters of the nation,
And our member, Mr. Hasset for to join the Galway Blazers.
REPEAT CHORUS

There were multitudes from Aran and members from New Quay shore,
The boys from Connemara and the Clare unmarried maidens.
There were people from Cork city who were loyal, true and faithful,
That brought home Fenian prisoners from dying in foreign nations.
REPEAT CHORUS

It's there you'll see confectioners with sugarsticks and dainties,
The lozenges and oranges, the lemonade and raisins.
The gingerbread and spices to accommodate the ladies,
And a big crubeen for threepence to be picking while you're able.
REPEAT CHORUS

It's there you'll see the gamblers, the thimbles and the garters,
And the sporting Wheel of Fortune with the four and twenty quarters.
There were others without scruple pelting wattles at poor Maggy,
And her father well contented and he looking at his daughter.
REPEAT CHORUS

It's there you'll see the pipers and the fiddlers competing,
And the nimble-footed dancers and they tripping on the daisies.
There were others crying 'Cigars and lights and bills of all the races
With the colours of the jockeys and the prize and horses' ages.'
REPEAT CHORUS

It's there you'd see the jockeys and they mounted on most stately,
The pink and blue, the red and green, the emblem of our nation.
When the bell was rung for starting all the horses seemed impatient,
I thought they never stood on ground, their speed was so amazing.
REPEAT CHORUS

There was half a million people there of all denominations,
The Catholic, the Protestant, the Jew and Presbyterian.
There was yet no animosity, no matter what persuasion,
But fáilte and hospitality inducing fresh acquaintance.
REPEAT CHORUS

THE JOLLY BEGGAR

G
It's of a jolly beggarman
             D
Came tripping o'er the plain,
     G   C
He came unto a farmer's door
  G   D
A lodging for to gain.
       G
The farmer's daughter she came down
              D
And viewed him cheek and chin,
G   C
She says, 'He is a handsome man,
  G   D
I pray you take him in.'

CHORUS:
G
We'll go no more a-roving,
       D
A-roving in the night,
 ·G   C
We'll go no more a-roving,
       G   D
Let the moon shine so bright,
G
We'll go no more a-roving.

He would not lie within the barn
Nor yet within the byre,
But he would in the corner lie
Down by the kitchen fire.
Oh, then the beggar's bed was made
Of good clean sheets and hay,
And down beside the kitchen fire
The jolly beggar lay.
REPEAT CHORUS

The farmer's daughter she got up
To bolt the kitchen door,
And there she saw the beggar
Standing naked on the floor.
He took the daughter in his arms
And to the bed he ran,
'Kind sir', she says, 'Be easy now,
You'll waken our good man.'
REPEAT CHORUS

'Now you are no beggar,
You are some gentleman,
For you have stolen my maidenhead
And I am quite undone.'
'I am no lord, I am no squire,
Of beggars I be one,
And beggars they be robbers all,
So you are quite undone.'
REPEAT CHORUS

*After chorus, repeat tune of last two lines
above with instead:*

She took her bed in both her hands
And threw it at the wall,
Says, 'Go with you the beggarman,
My maidenhead and all!'

JUG OF PUNCH

D
'Twas very early in the month of June,
       A   D
As I was sitting in my room,
               G   A
I heard a thrush sing in a bush,
          D   G   D
And the song it sang was the Jug of Punch.

CHORUS:
D   Em
Too-ra loo-ra loo, too-ra loo-ra loo,
        A   D
Too-ra loo-ra loo, too-ra loo-ra loo.
               G   A
I heard a thrush sing in a bush,
          D   G   D
And the song it sang was the Jug of Punch.

What more diversion can a man desire,
Than to be seated by a snug coal fire,
Upon his knee a pretty wench
And on the table a jug of punch
REPEAT CHORUS

If I were sick and very bad,
And was not able to go or stand,
I would not think it all amiss,
To pledge my shoes for a jug of punch.
REPEAT CHORUS

The doctor fails with all his art,
To cure an impression on the heart,
But if life was gone, within an inch,
What would bring it back but a jug of punch.
REPEAT CHORUS

But when I'm dead and in my grave,
No costly tombstone I will have,
But they'll dig a grave both wide and deep,
With a jug of punch at my head and feet.
REPEAT CHORUS

BEAUTIFUL CITY

D
I have sought to discover
  G   D
A haven of rest,
                   A
Where the sun sinks by night
            D
In the land of the West;

I have dwelt with the red man
  G   D
In green forest bow'rs,
  A
Or the wild rolling prairie
  A   D
Bespangled with flow'rs.

I have hied to the north,
      G   D
Where the hardy pine grows,
        A
'Mid the wolf and the bear,
        D
And the bleak winter snows;

I have roamed through all climates,
      G   D
But none could I see,
  A
Like the green hills of Cork
          D
And my home by the Lee.
                   A
Beautiful city, charming and pretty,
                   D
Beautiful city, my home by the Lee.

I have slumber'd in palm groves
By clear running streams,
And the wild groves of Blarney
Come haunting my dreams;
I have listened to bells
On the soft summer wind,
But the sweet bells of Shandon
Were dear to my mind:
I have mixed in gay dances
My sorrow to hide,
But there's none like the maiden
That's now by my side.
There is nought in the land
Of the slave or the free,
Like the green hills of Cork
And my home by the Lee.
Beautiful city, beautiful city,
Beautiful city, the pride of the Lee.

The bold feudal castle
Looks down on the Rhine,
That flows through the land
Of the olive and vine:
There's freedom and health
In the fresh mountain breeze,
That careers round the home
Of the brave Tyrolese;
There is beauty and love
In all spots of the earth,
To the heart that can call it
The land of its birth;
But of all the fair countries,
The dearest to me
Are the green hills of Cork
And my home by the Lee.
Beautiful city, beautiful city,
Beautiful city, the pride of the Lee.

PEGGY GORDON

D   G   D A
Oh, Peggy Gordon, you are my darling,
G   D   A
Come sit you down upon my knee
G   D   G   D A
And tell to me the very reason
G   D   A   D
Why I am slighted so by thee.

I wish I was in some lonesome valley,
Where womankind cannot be found,
Where the little birds sing upon the
branches,
And every moment a different sound.

Oh, Peggy Gordon, you are my darling,
Come sit you down upon my knee
And tell to me the very reason
Why I am slighted so by thee.

I'm so in love that I can't deny it,
My heart lies smothered in my breast,
But it's not for you to let the world know it,
A troubled mind can know no rest.

I put my head to a cask of brandy,
It was my fancy, I do declare,
For when I'm drinking, I'm always thinking,
And wishing Peggy Gordon was here.

THE COBBLER

```
D              A          D                        C
Oh, me name is Dick Darby I'm a cobbler, I served me time at old Camp,
    D        C    D                A          D
Some call me an old agitator, but now I'm resolved to repent.
```

CHORUS:
With me ing twing of an ing thing of an i-day,
With me ing twing of an ing thing of an i-day,
With me roo boo boo roo boo boo randy,
And me lap-stone keeps beating away.

Now my father was hung for sheep stealing, my mother was burned for a witch.
My sister's a dandy house-keeper, and I'm a mechanical switch.
REPEAT CHORUS

Ah, it's forty long years I have travelled all by the contents of me pack.
Me hammers, me awls and me pinchers, I carry them all on me back.
REPEAT CHORUS

Oh, my wife she is humpy, she's lumpy, my wife she's the devil, she's black.
And no matter what I may do with her, her tongue it goes clickety-clack.
REPEAT CHORUS

It was early one fine summer's morning, a little before it was day.
I dipped her three times in the river, and carelessly bade her 'Good day!'
REPEAT CHORUS

MY OWN DEAR GALWAY BAY

D   G   D
'Tis far away I am today

From scenes I roamed a boy
A   G
And long ago the hour I know
       A
I first saw Illinois,
            D   G
Nor time nor tide nor waters wide,
        A   D
Can wean my heart away,
         G   D
Forever true it flies to you,
      G   D
My own dear Galway Bay.

My chosen bride is by my side,
Her brown hair silver grey,
Her daughter Rose as like her grows
As April dawn to day;
Her eldest boy, his mother's joy,
His father's pride and stay,
With gifts like these, I'd live at ease,
Were I near Galway Bay.

A prouder man, I'd walk the land,
In health and peace of mind,
If I might toil and strive and moil,
Nor cast one thought behind;
But what would be the world to me,
Its wealth and rich array,
If memory I lost of thee, my poor old Galway Bay?

Oh grey and bleak, by shore and creek,
The rugged rocks abound,
But sweeter green the grass between
Than grows on Irish ground;
So friendship fond, all else beyond,
And love that lives always,
Bless each dear home, beside your foam,
My dear old Galway Bay.

Had I youth's blood, and hopeful mood,
And heart of fire once more,
For all the gold that earth might hold,
I'd never quit your shore;
I'd live content, whate'er God sent,
With neighbours old and grey,
And lay my bones, 'neath churchyard stones,
Beside you, Galway Bay.

The blessing of a poor old man
Be with you night and day,
The blessing of a lonely man
Whose heart will soon be clay;
'Tis all the heaven I ask of God, upon my dying day,
My soul to soar for ever more
Above you, Galway Bay.

FOLLOW ME UP TO CARLOW

Em
Lift Mac Cahir Og your face,

Brooding o'er the old disgrace

That black Fitzwilliam stormed your place
            D   Em
And drove you to the Fern.

Grey said victory was sure,

Soon the firebrand he'd secure;

Until he met at Glenmalure
           D   Em
Feach Mac Hugh O Byrne

CHORUS:
Em
Curse and swear Lord Kildare,
D
Feagh will do what Feach will dare
Em
Now Fitzwilliam, have a care,
D   Em
Fallen is your star, low.

Up with halbert, out with sword,
D
On we go forby the Lord
Em
Feach Mac Hugh has given his word,
D   Em
Follow me up to Carlow.

See the swords of Glen Imayle,
Flashing o'er the English Pale
See all the children of the Gael,
Beneath O'Byrne's banners.
Rooster of the fighting stock,
Would you let a fighting cock
Crow out upon an Irish rock,
Fly up and teach him manners.
REPEAT CHORUS

From Tassagart to Clonmore,
Flows a stream of Saxon Gore
Och, great is Rory Og O'More,
At sending loons to Hades.
White is sick and Lane is fled,
Now for black Fitzwilliam's head
We'll send it over, dripping red,
To Liza and the ladies
REPEAT CHORUS

THE BARD
OF ARMAGH

D   Em   D   A
Oh, list to the lay of a poor Irish harper
    D   A
And scorn not the strains
       A
Of his withered old hand,
    D   G
Remember his fingers,
    D   A
They once could move sharper,
    D   Em   A   D
To raise up the mem'ry of his dear native land.

When I was a young lad King Jamie did flourish
And I followed the wars
In my brogues bound with straw.
And all the fair colleens from Wexford to
Durrish
Called me bold Phelim Brady,
The Bard of Armagh.

How I love for to muse on the days of my
boyhood
Tho' four score and three years
Have flitted since then,
Still it gives sweet reflections
As every young joy should,
For light-hearted boys to make the best of old
men.

At pattern of fair I could twist my shillelagh
Or trip through the jig
With my brogues bound with straw,
Whilst all the pretty maidens
Around me assembled
Loving bold Phelim Brady,
The Bard of Armagh.

Although I have travelled
This wide world over,
Yet Erin's a home and a parent to me;
Then, oh, let the ground
That my old bones shall cover
Be cut from the soil that is trod by the free.

And when Sergeant Death
In his cold arms shall embrace me,
Oh, lull me to sleep with 'Erin go Bragh',
By the side of my Kathleen,
My young wife, oh, place me,
Then forget Phelim Brady,
The Bard of Armagh.

AS I ROVED OUT

Em   D
And who are you me pretty fair maid
Em
And who are you me honey, (repeat)
                      D
She answered me quite modestly:

'I am me mother's darling.'

CHORUS:
D   Em
With me too-ry-ay,
D
Fol de diddle day,
                   Em
Di-re, fol de diddle dair-ie oh.

And will you come to me mother's house
When the sun is shining clearly (repeat)
I'll open the door and I'll let you in
And divil a one would hear us.

So I went to her house in the middle of the
night
When the moon was shining clearly
(repeat)
She opened the door and she let me in
And divil the one did hear us.

She took me horse by the bridle and the bit
And she led him to the stable (repeat)
Saying, 'There's plenty of oats for a soldier's
horse,
To eat it if he's able.'

The she took me by the lily-white hand,
And she led me to the table (repeat)
Saying, 'There's plenty of wine for a soldier
boy,
To drink it if you're able.'

Then I got up and made the bed
And I made it nice and aisy (repeat)
Then I got up and laid her down,
Saying, 'Lassie, are you able?'

And there we lay till the break of day,
And divil a one did hear us (repeat)
Then I arose and put on me clothes,
Saying, 'Lassie, I must leave you.'

And when will you return again
And when will we get married (repeat)
When broken shells make Christmas bells
We might well get married.

HENRY MY SON

D
Where have you been all day, Henry my son?
                                  A
Where have you been all day, my beloved one?
D
Away in the meadow, away in the meadow,
               A   D
Make my bed I've a pain in my head
           A D
And I want to lie down.

And what did you have to eat, Henry my son?
What did you have to eat, my beloved one?
Poison beans, poison beans,
Make my bed I've a pain in my head
And I want to lie down.

And what colour were them beans, Henry my son?
What colour were them beans, my beloved one?
Green and yellow, green and yellow,
Make my bed I've a pain in my head
And I want to lie down.

And what will you leave your mother, Henry my son?
What will you leave your mother, my beloved one?
A woollen blanket, a woollen blanket,
Make my bed I've a pain in my head
And I want to lie down.

And what will you leave your children, Henry my son?
What will you leave your children, my beloved one?
The keys of heaven, the keys of heaven,
Make my bed I've a pain in my head
And I want to lie down.

And what will you leave your sweetheart, Henry my son?
What will you leave your sweetheart, my beloved one?
A rope to hang her, a rope to hang her,
Make my bed I've a pain in my head
And I want to lie down.

Feis Ceoil, Emo, Co. Laois, 1938

36

LANIGAN'S BALL

Am   G
In the town of Athy one Jeremy Lanigan, battered away till he hadn't a pound.
Am
His father he died and made him a man again, left him a farm and ten acres of ground.
                                                              G
He gave a grand party to friends and relations who did not forget him when come to the wall.
Am
If you but listen I'll make your eyes glisten at the rows and ructions at Lanigan's Ball.

CHORUS:

Am
Six long months I spent in Dublin, six long months doing nothing at all,

Six long months I spent in Dublin, learning to dance for Lanigan's ball.
                                    G
I stepped out, I stepped in again, I stepped out again, I stepped in again,
Am
I stepped out and I stepped in again, learning to dance for Lanigan's Ball.

Myself to be sure got free invitations, for all the nice girls and boys I might ask.
And just in a minute both friends and relations were dancing as merry as bees round a cask.
There was lashings of punch and wine for the ladies, potatoes and cakes, there was bacon and tea,
There were the Nolans, the Dolans, O'Gradys, courting the girls and dancing away.

They were doing all kinds of nonsensical polkas, all round the room in a whirligig,
But Julia and I soon banished their nonsense and tipped them a twist of a real Irish jig.
Oh, how that girl got mad on me, and danced till you'd think the ceilings would fall,
For I spent three weeks at Brooks Academy learning to dance for Lanigan's Ball.

Repeat chorus but add:

I stepped out, I stepped in again, I stepped in again and I stepped out again.
I stepped out, I stepped in again, learning to dance for Lanigan's Ball.

The boys were as merry, the girls all hearty, dancing away in couples and groups,
Till an accident happened; young Terence Mc Carthy, he put his right leg through Miss
Finnerty's hoops.
The creature she fainted and cried 'Meelia, murther', called for her brothers and gathered them all,
Carmody swore that he'd go no further, till he'd have satisfaction at Lanigan's Ball.

In the midst of the row, Miss Kerrigan fainted, her cheeks at the same time as red as a rose,
Some of the boys decried she was painted, she took a small drop too much, I suppose.
Her sweetheart Ned Morgan, so powerful and able, when he saw his fair colleen stretched
by the wall,
He tore the left leg from under the table and smashed all the dishes at Lanigan's Ball.
REPEAT CHORUS

Boys, oh boys 'tis then there was ructions myself got a kick from big Phelim Mc Hugh,
But soon I replied to his kind introduction and kicked up a terrible hullabaloo.
Ould Casey, the piper, was near being strangled, they squeezed up his pipes, bellows,
chanters and all.
The girls in their ribbons they all got entangled, and that put an end to Lanigan's Ball.
REPEAT CHORUS

THE TOWN OF BALLYBAY

D
In the town of Ballybay

There is a lassie dwelling,

I knew her very well
            A   D
And the story is worth telling.
           A
Her father kept a still
    D   A
And he was a good distiller,

When she took to drink, well
            D
The devil would not fill her,

CHORUS:

With my ring a ding a dum
           A
And me ring a ding a didios,
D
Me ring a ding a dum
A   D
Whack fol a ding daddios.

And she had a wooden leg
That was hollow down the middle
She used to tie a string on it
And play it like a fiddle.
She fiddled in the hall,
She fiddled in the alleyway,
She didn't give a damn,
She had to fiddle anyway.
REPEAT CHORUS

And she said she couldn't dance
Unless she had her wellie on,
But when she had it on
She could dance as well as anyone
She wouldn't go to bed
Unless she had her shimmy on
But when she had it on
She would go as quick as anyone.
REPEAT CHORUS

She had lovers by the score
Every Tom and Dick and Harry,
She was courting night and day
But still she wouldn't marry.
And then she fell in love
With a fella with a stammer,
When he tried to run away
She hit him with a hammer.
REPEAT CHORUS

She had childer up the stairs,
She had childer in the brier,
And another ten or twelve
Sitting roaring by the fire.
She fed them on potatoes
And on soup she made with nettles,
And on lumps of hairy bacon
That she boiled up in the kettle.
REPEAT CHORUS

So she led a sheltered life
Eating porridge and black pudding,
And she terrorised her man
Until he died right sudden.
And when the husband died
She was feeling very sorry,
She rolled him in a bag
And she threw him in a quarry.
REPEAT CHORUS

LOOK AT THE COFFIN

G   C
Look at the coffin with golden handles
     G   D
Isn't it grand boys to be bloodywell dead.

CHORUS:
G
Let's not have a sniffle,
           C   G
Let's all have a bloody good cry,
           C   G
And always remember the longer you live,
D   G
The sooner you'll bloodywell die.

Look at the flowers, all bloody withered,
Isn't it grand boys to be bloodywell dead.
REPEAT CHORUS

Look at the mourners, bloody great
hypocrites,
Isn't it grand boys to be bloodywell dead.
REPEAT CHORUS

Look at the preacher, bloody sanctimonious,
Isn't it grand boys to be bloodywell dead.
REPEAT CHORUS

JOHNNY I HARDLY KNEW YEH

Em
While going the road to sweet Athy,
　　G
Har-oo, har-oo,
　　Em
While going the road to sweet Athy,
　　G
Har-oo, har-oo,
　　　　　　D
While going the road to sweet Athy,
　C
A stick in my hand
　　D
And a tear in my eye,
　Em
A doleful damsel I heard cry,

'Johnny I hardly knew yeh.'

Chorus (to the same tune as verse above):
With drums and guns and guns and drums,
Ha-roo, ha-roo,
With drums and guns and guns and drums,
Ha-roo, ha-roo,
With drums and guns and guns and drums
The enemy nearly slew yeh,
My darling dear
You look so queer,
Johnny I hardly knew yeh.

Where are the eyes that looked so mild,
Ha-roo, ha-roo,
Where are the eyes that looked so mild,
Ha-roo, ha-roo,
Where are the eyes that looked so mild,
When my poor heart
You first beguiled,
Why did you skedaddle
From me and the child,
Johnny I hardly knew yeh.

Where are the legs with which you run,
Ha-roo, ha-roo
Where are the legs with which you run,
Ha-roo, ha-roo
Where are the legs with which you run,
When you went
To shoulder a gun,
Indeed your dancing
Days are done,
Johnny I hardly knew yeh.

It grieved my heart to see you sail,
Ha-roo, ha-roo
It grieved my heart to see you sail,
Ha-roo, ha-roo
It grieved my heart to see you sail
Though from my heart
You took leg-bail,
Like a cod you're doubled up
Head and tail,
Johnny I hardly knew yeh.

You haven't an arm and you haven't a leg,
Ha-roo, ha-roo
You haven't an arm and you haven't a leg,
Ha-roo, ha-roo
You haven't an arm and you haven't a leg,
You're an eyeless, noseless,
Chickenless egg,
You'll have to be put
In a bowl to beg,
Johnny I hardly knew yeh.

I'm happy for to see you home,
Ha-roo, ha-roo
I'm happy for to see you home,
Ha-roo, ha-roo
I'm happy for to see you home,
All from the island of Sulloon,
So low in the flesh
So high in the bone,
Johnny I hardly knew yeh.

But sad as it is to see you so,
Ha-roo, har-oo
But sad as it is to see you so,
Ha-roo, har-oo
But sad as it is to see you so,
And to think of you now
As an object of woe,
Your Peggy'll still keep you
On as her beau,
Johnny I hardly knew yeh.

ALSO AVAILABLE IN THIS SERIES:
Duncles 50 Great Irish Ballads Volume 1
Duncles 50 Great Irish Ballads Volume 3

VOLUME 1

SONNY'S DREAM
GRACE
TEDDY O'NEALE
WILD ROVER, THE
STREETS OF NEW YORK, THE
THE BAND PLAYED 'WALTZING MATHILDA'
MY LOVELY ROSE OF CLARE
MARY FROM DUNGLOE
THE LOWLANDS OF HOLLAND
EASY AND SLOW
DOWN BY THE GLENSIDE
THE CLIFFS OF DOONEEN
A NATION ONCE AGAIN
ARTHUR MC BRIDE
THE GLENDALOUGH SAINT
PADDY LAY BACK
THE GYPSY
IN DUBLIN'S FAIR CITY
THE ROSE OF MOONCOIN
THE RISING OF THE MOON
OLD MAID IN THE GARRET
NOVA SCOTIA
. . . . and many others

VOLUME 3

WORKING MAN
SPANCIL HILL
THE RARE OUL' TIMES,
WHEN YOU WERE SWEET SIXTEEN
NANCY SPAIN
THE GOOD SHIP KANGAROO
MONTO
NEW YORK GIRLS
SULLIVAN'S JOHN
WHISKEY IN THE JAR
DICEY REILLY
FAR AWAY IN AUSTRALIA
JAMES CONNOLLY
THE MERRY PLOUGHBOY
ST. PATRICK WAS A GENTLEMAN
BIG STRONG MAN (SYLVEST)
THE BOG DOWN IN THE VALLEY-O
HOME BOYS HOME
CARRICKFERGUS
THE FOGGY DEW
THE SPANISH LADY
THE WILD COLONIAL BOY
. . . . and many others

If you have stumbled your way through the chords in this book, you may like to know that Ossian has also published the following:

Basic Chords for Guitar and How to Use 'Em -
144 easy chords in all keys, with sections on tuning, strums, use of capo and a selection of easy songs.
By John Loesberg (OMB 59)

Instant Guitar Chords
864 chords - 24 chord types for every key, each shown in 3 positions on the neck. Suitable for Folk, Pop, Rock and Jazz.
By John Loesberg (OMB 60)

Chords for Mandolin/Irish Banjo/Bouzouki
Easy chords in all keys.
By John Loesberg (OMB 61)